Skillstreaming
in Early Childhood

REVISED EDITION

Program
Forms

New Strategies and Perspectives for Teaching Prosocial Skills

Ellen McGinnis
Arnold P. Goldstein

Research Press • 2612 North Mattis Avenue • Champaign, Illinois 61822
(800) 519-2707 • www.researchpress.com

Cover design by Linda Brown, Positive I.D. Graphic Design, Inc.
Printed by Bang Printing
Binding by SPI Binding Co., Inc.

ISBN 0–87822–475–0

CONTENTS

TEACHER/STAFF SKILLSTREAMING CHECKLIST

Student _____ Class/age _____

Teacher/staff _____ Date _____

INSTRUCTIONS: Listed below you will find a number of skills that children are more or less proficient in using. This checklist will help you evaluate how well each child uses the various skills. For each child, rate his/her use of each skill, based on your observations of his/her behavior in various situations.

Circle 1 if the child is *almost never* good at using the skill.

Circle 2 if the child is *seldom* good at using the skill.

Circle 3 if the child is *sometimes* good at using the skill.

Circle 4 if the child is *often* good at using the skill.

Circle 5 if the child is *almost always* good at using the skill.

Please rate the child on all skills listed. If you know of a situation in which the child has particular difficulty using the skill well, please note it briefly in the space marked "Problem situation."

	almost never	seldom	sometimes	often	almost always
1. **Listening:** Does the child appear to listen when someone is speaking and make an effort to understand what is said?	1	2	3	4	5
Problem situation:					
2. **Using Nice Talk:** Does the child speak to others in a friendly manner?	1	2	3	4	5
Problem situation:					
3. **Using Brave Talk:** Does the child use a brave or assertive tone of voice in a conflict with another child?	1	2	3	4	5
Problem situation:					
4. **Saying Thank You:** Does the child say thank you or in another way let others know he/she appreciates help given, favors, and so forth?	1	2	3	4	5
Problem situation:					
5. **Rewarding Yourself:** Does the child say when he/she has done a good job?	1	2	3	4	5
Problem situation:					

Skillstreaming in Early Childhood: New Strategies and Perspectives for Teaching Prosocial Skills
© 2003 by Ellen McGinnis and Arnold P. Goldstein. Champaign, IL: Research Press (800) 519–2707.

6. **Asking for Help:** Does the child request help when needed in an acceptable manner?

         1   2   3   4   5

Problem situation:

7. **Asking a Favor:** Does the child ask favors of others in an acceptable way?

         1   2   3   4   5

Problem situation:

8. **Ignoring:** Does the child ignore other children or situations when it is desirable to do so?

         1   2   3   4   5

Problem situation:

9. **Asking a Question:** Does the child ask questions about something he/she doesn't understand?

         1   2   3   4   5

Problem situation:

10. **Following Directions:** Does the child seem to understand directions and follow them?

         1   2   3   4   5

Problem situation:

11. **Trying When It's Hard:** Does the child continue to try when something is difficult instead of giving up?

         1   2   3   4   5

Problem situation:

12. **Interrupting:** Does the child interrupt when necessary in an appropriate manner?

         1   2   3   4   5

Problem situation:

13. **Greeting Others:** Does the child acknowledge acquaintances when it is appropriate to do so?

         1   2   3   4   5

Problem situation:

14. **Reading Others:** Does the child pay attention to a person's nonverbal language and seem to understand what is being communicated?

         1   2   3   4   5

Problem situation:

15. **Joining In:** Does the child use acceptable ways of joining in an ongoing activity or group?

         1   2   3   4   5

Problem situation:

Skillstreaming in Early Childhood: New Strategies and Perspectives for Teaching Prosocial Skills
© 2003 by Ellen McGinnis and Arnold P. Goldstein. Champaign, IL: Research Press (800) 519–2707.

	almost never	seldom	sometimes	often	almost always

16. **Waiting Your Turn:** Does the child wait his/her turn when playing a game with others?   1   2   3   4   5

Problem situation:

17. **Sharing:** Does the child share most materials and toys with peers?   1   2   3   4   5

Problem situation:

18. **Offering Help:** Does the child recognize when someone needs or wants help and offer assistance?   1   2   3   4   5

Problem situation:

19. **Asking Someone to Play:** Does the child ask other children to play or extend an invitation to others to join in his/her activity?   1   2   3   4   5

Problem situation:

20. **Playing a Game:** Does the child play games with peers in a fair manner?   1   2   3   4   5

Problem situation:

21. **Knowing Your Feelings:** Does the child identify his/her feelings?   1   2   3   4   5

Problem situation:

22. **Feeling Left Out:** Does the child deal with being left out of an activity without losing control or becoming upset?   1   2   3   4   5

Problem situation:

23. **Asking to Talk:** Does the child verbally express when he/she seems upset?   1   2   3   4   5

Problem situation:

24. **Dealing with Fear:** When afraid, does the child know why he/she is afraid and deal with this fear in an acceptable way (e.g., by talking about it)?   1   2   3   4   5

Problem situation:

25. **Deciding How Someone Feels:** Does the child identify how another person appears to be feeling by what the person says?   1   2   3   4   5

Problem situation:

Skillstreaming in Early Childhood: New Strategies and Perspectives for Teaching Prosocial Skills
© 2003 by Ellen McGinnis and Arnold P. Goldstein. Champaign, IL: Research Press (800) 519–2707.

26. **Showing Affection:** Does the child show that he/she likes someone in an acceptable way?

    Problem situation:

          1   2   3   4   5

27. **Dealing with Teasing:** Does the child deal with being teased in acceptable ways?

    Problem situation:

          1   2   3   4   5

28. **Dealing with Feeling Mad:** Does the child use acceptable ways to express his/her anger?

    Problem situation:

          1   2   3   4   5

29. **Deciding If It's Fair:** Does the child accurately assess what is fair and unfair?

    Problem situation:

          1   2   3   4   5

30. **Solving a Problem:** When a problem occurs, does the child state alternative, prosocial ways to solve the problem?

    Problem situation:

          1   2   3   4   5

31. **Accepting Consequences:** Does the child accept the consequences for his/her behavior without becoming angry or upset?

    Problem situation:

          1   2   3   4   5

32. **Relaxing:** Is the child able to relax when tense or upset?

    Problem situation:

          1   2   3   4   5

33. **Dealing with Mistakes:** Does the child accept making mistakes without becoming upset?

    Problem situation:

          1   2   3   4   5

34. **Being Honest:** Is the child honest when confronted with a negative behavior?

    Problem situation:

          1   2   3   4   5

35. **Knowing When to Tell:** Does the child refrain from telling on others about small problems?

    Problem situation:

          1   2   3   4   5

		almost never	seldom	sometimes	often	almost always

36. **Dealing with Losing:** Does the child accept losing at a game or activity without becoming upset or angry?   1 2 3 4 5

Problem situation:

37. **Wanting to Be First:** Does the child accept not being first at a game or activity?   1 2 3 4 5

Problem situation:

38. **Saying No:** Does the child say no in an acceptable manner to things he/she doesn't want to do or to things that may get him/her into trouble?   1 2 3 4 5

Problem situation:

39. **Accepting No:** Does the child accept being told no without becoming upset?   1 2 3 4 5

Problem situation:

40. **Deciding What to Do:** Does the child choose acceptable activities on his/her own when feeling bored?   1 2 3 4 5

Problem situation:

PARENT SKILLSTREAMING CHECKLIST

Name _____ Date _____

Child's name _____ Birth date _____

INSTRUCTIONS: Based on your observations in various situations, rate your child's use of the following skills.

Circle 1 if the child is *almost never* good at using the skill.

Circle 2 if the child is *seldom* good at using the skill.

Circle 3 if the child is *sometimes* good at using the skill.

Circle 4 if the child is *often* good at using the skill.

Circle 5 if the child is *almost always* good at using the skill.

	almost never	seldom	sometimes	often	almost always
1. **Listening:** Does your child listen and understand when you or others talk to him/her? Comments:	1	2	3	4	5
2. **Using Nice Talk:** Does your child speak to others in a friendly manner? Comments:	1	2	3	4	5
3. **Using Brave Talk:** Does your child use a brave or assertive tone of voice in a conflict with another child? Comments:	1	2	3	4	5
4. **Saying Thank You:** Does your child say thank you or in another way show thanks when someone does something nice for him/her? Comments:	1	2	3	4	5
5. **Rewarding Yourself:** Does your child tell you when he/she has done a good job? Comments:	1	2	3	4	5
6. **Asking for Help:** Does your child ask in a friendly way when he/she needs help? Comments:	1	2	3	4	5

7. **Asking a Favor:** Does your child ask favors of others in an acceptable way?

    Comments:

    1 2 3 4 5

8. **Ignoring:** Does your child ignore other children or situations when it is desirable to ignore them?

    Comments:

    1 2 3 4 5

9. **Asking a Question:** Does your child ask questions about something he/she doesn't understand?

    Comments:

    1 2 3 4 5

10. **Following Directions:** Does your child seem to understand and follow directions that you give?

    Comments:

    1 2 3 4 5

11. **Trying When It's Hard:** Does your child continue to try when something is difficult instead of giving up?

    Comments:

    1 2 3 4 5

12. **Interrupting:** Does your child know when and how to interrupt when he/she needs something?

    Comments:

    1 2 3 4 5

13. **Greeting Others:** Does your child acknowledge acquaintances when it is appropriate to do so?

    Comments:

    1 2 3 4 5

14. **Reading Others:** Does your child pay attention to a person's nonverbal language and seem to understand what is being communicated?

    Comments:

    1 2 3 4 5

15. **Joining In:** Does your child use acceptable ways of joining in an activity with friends or family?

    Comments:

    1 2 3 4 5

16. **Waiting Your Turn:** Does your child wait his/her turn when playing a game with others?

    Comments:

    1 2 3 4 5

17. **Sharing:** Does your child share most materials and toys with his/her friends?

Comments:

1 2 3 4 5

18. **Offering Help:** Does your child recognize when someone needs or wants help and offer this help?

Comments:

1 2 3 4 5

19. **Asking Someone to Play:** Does your child ask other children to play or join in his/her activity?

Comments:

1 2 3 4 5

20. **Playing a Game:** Does your child play games with friends in a fair manner?

Comments:

1 2 3 4 5

21. **Knowing Your Feelings:** Does your child identify his/her feelings?

Comments:

1 2 3 4 5

22. **Feeling Left Out:** Does your child deal with being left out of an activity without losing control or becoming upset?

Comments:

1 2 3 4 5

23. **Asking to Talk:** Does your child talk about his/her problems when upset?

Comments:

1 2 3 4 5

24. **Dealing with Fear:** Does your child know why he/she is afraid and deal with this fear in an acceptable way (e.g., by talking about it)?

Comments:

1 2 3 4 5

25. **Deciding How Someone Feels:** Does your child identify how another person appears to be feeling by what the person says?

Comments:

1 2 3 4 5

26. **Showing Affection:** Does your child show that he/she likes someone in an acceptable way?

Comments:

1 2 3 4 5

Skillstreaming in Early Childhood: New Strategies and Perspectives for Teaching Prosocial Skills
© 2003 by Ellen McGinnis and Arnold P. Goldstein. Champaign, IL: Research Press (800) 519–2707.

27. **Dealing with Teasing:** Does your child deal with being teased in acceptable ways?

          1   2   3   4   5

Comments:

28. **Dealing with Feeling Mad:** Does your child use acceptable ways to express his/her anger?

          1   2   3   4   5

Comments:

29. **Deciding If It's Fair:** Does your child accurately assess what is fair and unfair?

          1   2   3   4   5

Comments:

30. **Solving a Problem:** When a problem occurs, does your child state alternative, acceptable ways to solve the problem?

          1   2   3   4   5

Comments:

31. **Accepting Consequences:** Does your child accept the consequences for his/her behavior without becoming angry or upset?

          1   2   3   4   5

Comments:

32. **Relaxing:** Is your child able to relax when tense or upset?

          1   2   3   4   5

Comments:

33. **Dealing with Mistakes:** Does your child accept making mistakes without becoming upset?

          1   2   3   4   5

Comments:

34. **Being Honest:** Does your child admit that he/she has done something wrong when confronted?

          1   2   3   4   5

Comments:

35. **Knowing When to Tell:** Does your child refrain from telling on others about small problems?

          1   2   3   4   5

Comments:

36. **Dealing with Losing:** Does your child accept losing at a game or activity without becoming upset or angry?

          1   2   3   4   5

Comments:

	almost never	seldom	sometimes	often	almost always
37. **Wanting to Be First:** Does your child accept not being first at a game or activity? Comments:	1	2	3	4	5
38. **Saying No:** Does your child say no in an acceptable way to things he/she doesn't want to do or to things that may get him/her into trouble? Comments:	1	2	3	4	5
39. **Accepting No:** Does your child accept being told no without becoming upset? Comments:	1	2	3	4	5
40. **Deciding What to Do:** Does your child choose acceptable activities on his/her own when feeling bored? Comments:	1	2	3	4	5

Skillstreaming in Early Childhood: New Strategies and Perspectives for Teaching Prosocial Skills
© 2003 by Ellen McGinnis and Arnold P. Goldstein. Champaign, IL: Research Press (800) 519–2707.

CHILD SKILLSTREAMING CHECKLIST

INSTRUCTIONS: Ask the child to point to the picture on the Child Skillstreaming Response Record corresponding to each question (rabbit, teddy bear, cat, etc.), listen carefully as you read the question, then color the face that shows how he/she feels. Repeat each question at least once.

SESSION 1

1. **Skill 1/rabbit:** Is it easy for you to listen and understand when someone is talking to you?

2. **Skill 2/teddy bear:** Is it easy for you to talk to others in a friendly way?

3. **Skill 3/cat:** Do you tell a person to stop when that person is bothering you without getting upset or mad?

4. **Skill 4/owl:** Do you say thank you or show thanks when someone has said or done something nice for you?

5. **Skill 5/elephant:** Do you tell about things that you do a good job with?

6. **Skill 6/flower:** Is it easy for you to ask in a friendly way when you need help?

7. **Skill 7/pig:** Is it easy for you to ask a favor of someone else?

8. **Skill 8/mouse:** Do you ignore others when they are acting silly?

9. **Skill 9/dog:** Do you ask questions about things you don't understand?

10. **Skill 10/bird:** Do you know what to do when directions are given?

SESSION 2

1. **Skill 11/rabbit:** Do you keep trying when something is hard to do?

2. **Skill 12/teddy bear:** When you want or need something from a teacher or parent who is busy, do you interrupt in a nice way?

3. **Skill 13/cat:** When you walk by somebody you know a little bit, do you smile and say hi?

4. **Skill 14/owl:** Can you tell when someone is sad or mad by how the person looks?

5. **Skill 15/elephant:** Is it easy for you to join in a game if you want to play?

6. **Skill 16/flower:** Is it easy for you to wait your turn when playing a game?

7. **Skill 17/pig:** Is it easy for you to share toys with friends?

8. **Skill 18/mouse:** Do you notice when someone needs or wants help and try to help the person?

9. **Skill 19/dog:** Is it easy for you to ask a friend to play?

10. **Skill 20/bird:** When playing a game, do you play fair?

Session 3

1. **Skill 21/rabbit:** Is it easy for you to say how you feel (mad, happy, frustrated)?

2. **Skill 22/teddy bear:** Do you still feel OK if you are left out of a game or activity?

3. **Skill 23/cat:** When you feel upset, is it easy for you to talk about why you're upset?

4. **Skill 24/owl:** When you feel afraid, do you talk to somebody about it?

5. **Skill 25/elephant:** Can you tell if somebody else is feeling mad, sad, or afraid by what the person says?

6. **Skill 26/flower:** Is it easy for you to show the people you like that you like them?

7. **Skill 27/pig:** When somebody teases you, can you keep from being upset?

8. **Skill 28/mouse:** Is it easy for you to stay in control when you are mad?

9. **Skill 29/dog:** Can you tell what is fair or not fair?

10. **Skill 30/bird:** If a problem happens, can you think of different ways to handle it—ways that won't get you into trouble?

Session 4

1. **Skill 31/rabbit:** Do you accept your punishment when you've done something wrong without getting mad or upset?

2. **Skill 32/teddy bear:** When you feel tense or upset, is it easy for you to calm down?

3. **Skill 33/cat:** When you make a mistake on an activity or in a game, do you still feel OK?

4. **Skill 34/owl:** Do you tell the truth if you have done something wrong?

5. **Skill 35/elephant:** Can you keep from telling on someone else who does something wrong?

6. **Skill 36/flower:** If you lose at a game, can you keep from becoming upset or angry?

7. **Skill 37/pig:** Do you still feel OK if you are not first at a game or activity?

8. **Skill 38/mouse:** Is it easy to say no to something a friend wants you to do that you don't want to do or that might get you into trouble?

9. **Skill 39/dog:** When you are told no to something you want to do, can you keep from becoming upset?

10. **Skill 40/bird:** When you feel bored, can you choose something to do?

CHILD SKILLSTREAMING RESPONSE RECORD

Name _____ Birth date _____

School/program _____

Teacher/evaluator _____ Assessment date _____

1.

2.

3.

4.

SKILLSTREAMING GROUPING CHART

	student names														
GROUP I: Beginning Social Skills															
1. Listening															
2. Using Nice Talk															
3. Using Brave Talk															
4. Saying Thank You															
5. Rewarding Yourself															
6. Asking for Help															
7. Asking a Favor															
8. Ignoring															
GROUP II: School-Related Skills															
9. Asking a Question															
10. Following Directions															
11. Trying When It's Hard															
12. Interrupting															
GROUP III: Friendship-Making Skills															
13. Greeting Others															
14. Reading Others															
15. Joining In															
16. Waiting Your Turn															
17. Sharing															
18. Offering Help															
19. Asking Someone to Play															
20. Playing a Game															
GROUP IV: Dealing with Feelings															
21. Knowing Your Feelings															
22. Feeling Left Out															
23. Asking to Talk															
24. Dealing with Fear															
25. Deciding How Someone Feels															
26. Showing Affection															

Skillstreaming in Early Childhood: New Strategies and Perspectives for Teaching Prosocial Skills
© 2003 by Ellen McGinnis and Arnold P. Goldstein. Champaign, IL: Research Press (800) 519–2707.

	student names																			
GROUP V: Alternatives to Aggression																				
27. Dealing with Teasing																				
28. Dealing with Feeling Mad																				
29. Deciding If It's Fair																				
30. Solving a Problem																				
31. Accepting Consequences																				
GROUP VI: Dealing with Stress																				
32. Relaxing																				
33. Dealing with Mistakes																				
34. Being Honest																				
35. Knowing When to Tell																				
36. Dealing with Losing																				
37. Wanting to Be First																				
38. Saying No																				
39. Accepting No																				
40. Deciding What to Do																				

Skillstreaming in Early Childhood: New Strategies and Perspectives for Teaching Prosocial Skills
© 2003 by Ellen McGinnis and Arnold P. Goldstein. Champaign, IL: Research Press (800) 519–2707.

SKILLSTREAMING IN EARLY CHILDHOOD RUBRIC

Student name _____ Date _____

Evaluator name _____ Position _____

DIRECTIONS: Circle the number corresponding to your best assessment of the child's skills. Pre- and post-assessment may be completed by circling the number corresponding to skill proficiency in different colors. The specific area of concern (i.e., Academic, Peer Relations, Self-Control, Assertion, or Cooperation) may be circled or highlighted to indicate problematic situations and areas for instruction.

A. Listens (Academic; Cooperation; Peer Relations).

    4. Consistently and actively listens to others in almost all academic and behavioral group situations and seems to understand what is said.

    3. Consistently listens to others in most academic and behavioral situations and most of the time seems to understand what is being said.

    2. Sporadically demonstrates listening and understanding in some group and individual academic and behavioral situations.

    1. Rarely, if ever, demonstrates listening behaviors in any situation or setting.

    Skills for instruction: Skill 1 (Listening)

                            Skill 8 (Ignoring)

B. Speaks to others in friendly or assertive ways (Academic; Peer Relations).

    4. Consistently speaks to others in friendly or assertive ways appropriate to the social or academic situation.

    3. Most of the time speaks to others in friendly or assertive ways appropriate to the social or academic situation.

    2. Sporadically is able to speak to others in friendly or assertive ways in some social or academic situations.

    1. Rarely, if ever, is able to speak to others appropriately in social or academic situations.

    Skills for instruction: Skill 2 (Using Nice Talk)

                            Skill 3 (Using Brave Talk)

                            Skill 14 (Reading Others)

C. Asks for help or favors when needed (Academic; Assertion; Peer Relations).

    4. Consistently asks for help or favors in appropriate ways whenever needed in academic and social situations.

    3. Most of the time asks for help or favors in appropriate ways when needed in most academic and social situations.

    2. Sporadically asks for help or favors in appropriate ways when needed in some academic and social situations.

    1. Rarely, if ever, asks for help or favors appropriately when needed.

Skills for instruction: Skill 6 (Asking for Help)

Skill 7 (Asking a Favor)

Skill 23 (Asking to Talk)

D. Expresses appreciation (Academic; Peer Relations).

4. Consistently thanks others for help or favors given in appropriate ways in almost all academic and social situations.

3. Most of the time thanks others for help or favors given in appropriate ways in most academic and social situations.

2. Occasionally thanks others for help or favors given in appropriate ways in some academic and social situations.

1. Rarely, if ever, thanks others appropriately for help or favors given in either academic or social situations.

Skill for instruction: Skill 4 (Saying Thank You)

E. Evaluates own performance (Academic; Self-Control; Assertion).

4. Consistently and accurately identifies and rewards self for a job well done.

3. Most of the time identifies when a job is well done and rewards self appropriately.

2. Occasionally identifies when a job is well done and rewards self appropriately.

1. Rarely, if ever, identifies when a job is well done and rewards self appropriately.

Skill for instruction: Skill 5 (Rewarding Yourself)

F. Avoids problematic or conflict situations by ignoring (Peer Relations; Academic; Self-Control; Cooperation).

4. Consistently ignores distracting or problematic peer behavior in academic and social situations when it is appropriate to do so.

3. Most of the time ignores distracting or problematic peer behavior in most academic and social situations when it is appropriate to do so.

2. Occasionally ignores distracting or problematic peer behavior in some academic and social situations when it is appropriate to do so.

1. Rarely, if ever, ignores distracting or problematic peer behavior in any situation.

Skills for instruction: Skill 8 (Ignoring)

Skill 35 (Knowing When to Tell)

G. Follows directions and completes tasks (Academic; Self-Control; Cooperation).

4. Consistently follows directions in almost all academic and cooperative situations, asking questions to clarify and following through to the completion of the task or direction.

3. Most of the time follows directions in most academic and cooperative situations, asking questions to clarify and following through to the completion of the task or direction.

2. Occasionally follows directions in some academic and cooperative situations, at times asking questions to clarify and occasionally following through to the completion of the task or direction.

1. Rarely, if ever, follows directions, asks clarifying questions, or completes tasks.

Skillstreaming in Early Childhood: New Strategies and Perspectives for Teaching Prosocial Skills
© 2003 by Ellen McGinnis and Arnold P. Goldstein. Champaign, IL: Research Press (800) 519–2707.

Skills for instruction: Skill 9 (Asking a Question)

   Skill 10 (Following Directions)

   Skill 11 (Trying When It's Hard)

H. Interrupts appropriately and under appropriate circumstances (Self-Control; Academic; Assertion).

   4. Consistently interrupts others appropriately when necessary in social and academic situations.

   3. Most of the time interrupts others appropriately when necessary in social and academic situations.

   2. Occasionally interrupts others appropriately when necessary in social and academic situations.

   1. Rarely, if ever, interrupts in an appropriate manner.

   Skills for instruction: Skill 12 (Interrupting)

   Skill 35 (Knowing When to Tell)

I. Initiates contacts with others (Peer Relations; Assertion).

   4. Consistently and actively acknowledges others and joins in activities in the classroom or with peers in an appropriate and natural manner.

   3. Most of the time acknowledges others and joins in activities in the classroom or with peers in an appropriate and natural manner.

   2. Occasionally acknowledges others and sometimes joins in activities in the classroom or with peers in a somewhat appropriate manner.

   1. Rarely, if ever, initiates interaction with others in an appropriate manner.

   Skills for instruction: Skill 13 (Greeting Others)

   Skill 15 (Joining In)

   Skill 19 (Asking Someone to Play)

J. Is sensitive to nonverbal communication (Peer Relations; Self-Control).

   4. Consistently demonstrates understanding of and insight about the nonverbal communication of others in almost all situations.

   3. Most of the time demonstrates understanding of and insight about the nonverbal communication of others in most situations.

   2. Occasionally demonstrates understanding of and insight about the nonverbal communication of others in some situations.

   1. Rarely, if ever, demonstrates understanding and insight, misreading others' nonverbal communication.

   Skills for instruction: Skill 14 (Reading Others)

   Skill 25 (Deciding How Someone Feels)

   Skill 28 (Dealing with Feeling Mad)

K. Plays appropriately with others (Academic; Peer Relations; Self-Control; Assertion; Cooperation).

    4. Consistently and actively cooperates with others during almost all academic or social games.

    3. Most of the time cooperates with others during academic or social games.

    2. Occasionally cooperates with others during academic or social games.

    1. Rarely, if ever, cooperates with others during academic or social games.

    Skills for instruction: Skill 16 (Waiting Your Turn)

                    Skill 17 (Sharing)

                    Skill 20 (Playing a Game)

                    Skill 36 (Dealing with Losing)

                    Skill 37 (Wanting to Be First)

L. Understands the feelings of others (Peer Relations; Cooperation; Self-Control).

    4. Consistently and actively seeks to understand the feelings of another in almost all appropriate situations when that person is experiencing a problem.

    3. Most of the time actively seeks to understand the feelings of another in most appropriate situations when that person is experiencing a problem.

    2. Occasionally seeks to understand the feelings of another in most appropriate situations when that person is experiencing a problem.

    1. Rarely, if ever, notices or seeks to understand the feelings of another.

    Skill for instruction: Skill 25 (Deciding How Someone Feels)

M. Demonstrates empathy (Peer Relations; Cooperation).

    4. Consistently and actively demonstrates empathy toward another when that person is upset or sad.

    3. Most of the time demonstrates empathy toward another when that person is upset or sad.

    2. Occasionally demonstrates empathy toward another when that person is upset or sad.

    1. Rarely, if ever, demonstrates empathy toward another.

    Skills for instruction: Skill 18 (Offering Help)

                    Skill 26 (Showing Affection)

N. Identifies own feelings (Self-Control).

    4. Consistently identifies own feelings in appropriate situations.

    3. Most of the time identifies own feelings in appropriate situations.

    2. Occasionally identifies own feelings in appropriate situations.

    1. Rarely, if ever, identifies own feelings.

    Skill for instruction: Skill 21 (Knowing Your Feelings)

O. Identifies feelings appropriate to a situation (Assertion; Peer Relations; Academic; Self-Control).

    4. Consistently interprets situations accurately and identifies appropriate feelings.

    3. Most of the time interprets situations accurately and identifies appropriate feelings.

Skillstreaming in Early Childhood: New Strategies and Perspectives for Teaching Prosocial Skills
© 2003 by Ellen McGinnis and Arnold P. Goldstein. Champaign, IL: Research Press (800) 519–2707.

2. Occasionally interprets situations accurately and identifies appropriate feelings.

1. Rarely, if ever, interprets situations accurately and identifies appropriate feelings.

Skills for instruction: Skill 11 (Trying When It's Hard)

                                Skill 14 (Reading Others)

                                Skill 21 (Knowing Your Feelings)

                                Skill 22 (Feeling Left Out)

                                Skill 24 (Dealing with Fear)

                                Skill 28 (Dealing with Feeling Mad)

                                Skill 33 (Dealing with Mistakes)

                                Skill 36 (Dealing with Losing)

P. Shows affection (Peer Relations; Cooperation).

4. Consistently displays affection appropriate to the person and in appropriate ways when it is relevant to do so.

3. Most of the time displays affection appropriate to the person and in appropriate ways when it is relevant to do so.

2. Occasionally displays affection appropriate to the person and in appropriate ways when it is relevant to do so.

1. Rarely, if ever, displays affection appropriately when it is relevant to do so.

Skill for instruction: Skill 26 (Showing Affection)

Q. Deals with anger and conflict (Self-Control; Peer Relations; Cooperation).

4. Consistently deals with anger and conflict appropriately in almost all situations.

3. Most of the time deals with anger and conflict appropriately in most situations.

2. Occasionally deals with anger and conflict appropriately in some situations.

1. Rarely, if ever, deals with anger and conflict appropriately in any situation.

Skills for instruction: Skill 23 (Asking to Talk)

                                Skill 28 (Dealing with Feeling Mad)

                                Skill 30 (Solving a Problem)

                                Skill 31 (Accepting Consequences)

                                Skill 32 (Relaxing)

                                Skill 33 (Dealing with Mistakes)

                                Skill 39 (Accepting No)

R. Deals with peer provocation (Self-Control; Peer Relations).

4. Consistently deals with peer provocation in productive ways.

3. Most of the time deals with peer provocation in productive ways.

2. Occasionally deals with peer provocation in productive ways.

1. Rarely, if ever, deals with peer provocation in productive ways.

Skills for instruction: Skill 23 (Asking to Talk)

Skill 27 (Dealing with Teasing)

Skill 35 (Knowing When to Tell)

S. Decides what is fair (Self-Control; Peer Relations).

4. Consistently and accurately assesses what is fair and unfair in almost all situations when appropriate.

3. Most of the time accurately assesses what is fair and unfair in most situations when appropriate.

2. Occasionally accurately assesses what is fair and unfair in some situations when appropriate.

1. Rarely, if ever, accurately assesses what is fair and unfair.

Skill for instruction: Skill 29 (Deciding If It's Fair)

T. Accepts consequences (Self-Control; Cooperation; Academic).

4. Consistently accepts consequences of own actions appropriately in almost all situations.

3. Most of the time accepts consequences of own actions appropriately in most situations.

2. Occasionally accepts consequences of own actions appropriately in some situations.

1. Rarely, if ever, accepts consequences of own actions appropriately.

Skills for instruction: Skill 31 (Accepting Consequences)

Skill 32 (Relaxing)

Skill 33 (Dealing with Mistakes)

Skill 34 (Being Honest)

U. Resists peer pressure (Cooperation; Peer Relations; Self-Control).

4. Consistently says no in an acceptable manner to things he/she doesn't want to do or to things that may be trouble.

3. Most of the time says no in an acceptable manner to things he/she doesn't want to do or to things that may be trouble.

2. Occasionally says no in an acceptable manner to things he/she doesn't want to do or to things that may be trouble.

1. Rarely, if ever, says no in an acceptable manner to things he/she doesn't want to do or to things that may be trouble.

Skills for instruction: Skill 29 (Deciding If It's Fair)

Skill 30 (Solving a Problem)

Skill 38 (Saying No)

V. Accepts being told no (Cooperation; Peer Relations; Self-Control).

4. Consistently accepts being told no in an acceptable way.

3. Most of the time accepts being told no in an acceptable way.

2. Occasionally accepts being told no in an acceptable way.

1. Rarely, if ever, accepts being told no in an acceptable way.

Skill for instruction: Skill 39 (Accepting No)

Skillstreaming in Early Childhood: New Strategies and Perspectives for Teaching Prosocial Skills
© 2003 by Ellen McGinnis and Arnold P. Goldstein. Champaign, IL: Research Press (800) 519–2707.

W. Uses free time appropriately (Cooperation; Assertion).

    4. Consistently selects acceptable activities when feeling bored.

    3. Most of the time selects acceptable activities when feeling bored.

    2. Occasionally selects acceptable activities when feeling bored.

    1. Rarely, if ever, selects acceptable activities when feeling bored.

    Skill for instruction: Skill 40 (Deciding What to Do)

HOMEWORK 1 REPORT

Name _____ Date _____

Skill _____

STEPS

_____

Who?   When?

_____

How I did

HOMEWORK 2 REPORT

Name _____ Date _____

Skill _____

STEPS

_____

I did it!

I reached
my goal!

Name _____

Date _____

Skill _____

Great job!

Name _____

Date _____

Skill _____

Good for me!

Name _____

Date _____

Skill _____

Together we can!

Skill _____

We can do it!

Skill _____

Skill Ticket

Name

Skill Ticket

Name

Skill Ticket

Name

Skill Ticket

Name

Skill Ticket

Name

Skill Ticket

Name

Skill Ticket

Name

Skill Ticket

Name

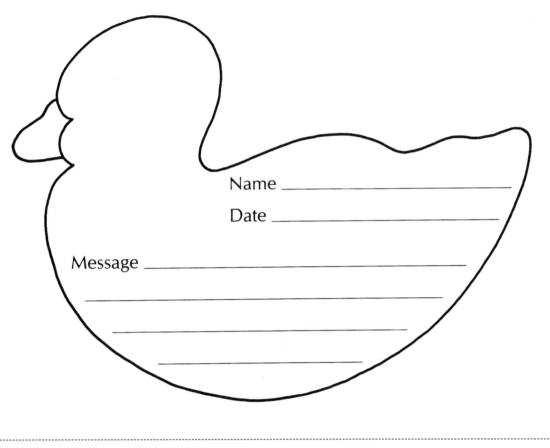

Name _____

Date _____

Message _____

_____

_____

_____

Name _____

Date _____

Message _____

_____

_____

_____

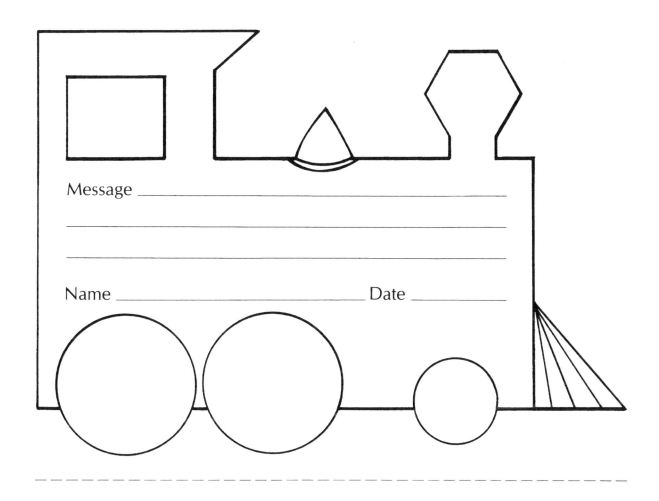

Message _____

_____

_____

Name _____ Date _____

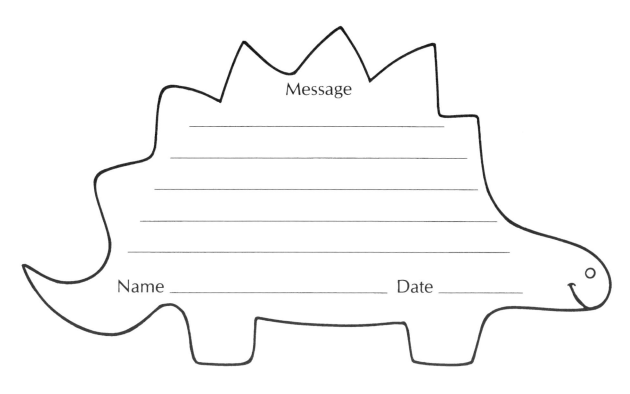

Message

_____

_____

_____

_____

Name _____ Date _____

Award

Name _____

Date _____

School Skills Award

Name _____

Date _____

Friendship Award

Name _____

Date _____

Dealing with Feelings Award

Name _____

Date _____

Keeping Your Cool Award

Name _____

Date _____

Skillstreaming in Early Childhood: New Strategies and Perspectives for Teaching Prosocial Skills
© 2003 by Ellen McGinnis and Arnold P. Goldstein. Champaign, IL: Research Press (800) 519–2707.

Dealing with Stress Award

Name _____

Date _____

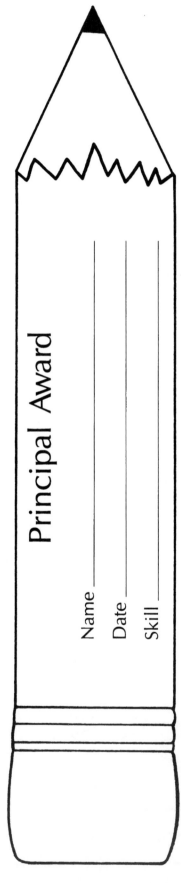

Principal Award

Name _____

Date _____

Skill _____

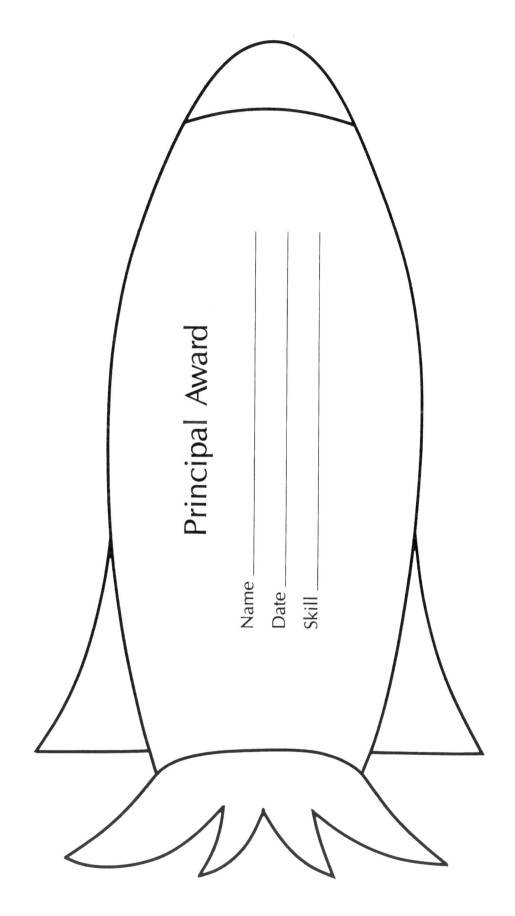

Principal Award

Name _____

Date _____

Skill _____

Parent Award

Name _____

Date _____

Parent Signature _____

Skill

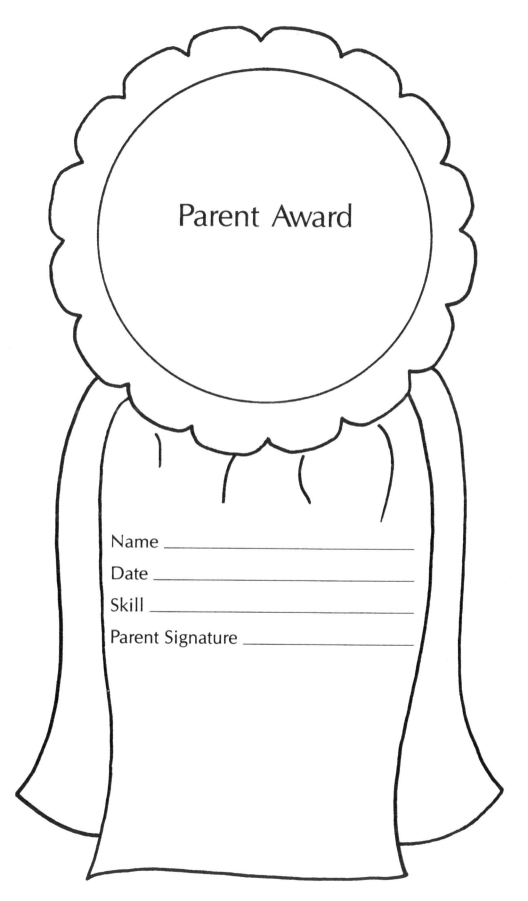

Parent Award

Name _____

Date _____

Skill _____

Parent Signature _____

PARENT ORIENTATION NOTE

Date _____

Dear Parent or Guardian:

Your child and his or her classmates are learning to handle a variety of day-to-day concerns in positive ways. Sharing, taking turns, handling teasing and anger, and following directions are some of the concerns we are working on. We are all learning specific steps to social skills in order to handle these problems in acceptable ways.

The process we are using to learn these skills is called Skillstreaming. First, your child is watching someone else use the skill. Then he or she will try out the skill and receive feedback about how well he or she performed the skill from both peers and adults. Finally, your child will be asked to practice the skill in real-life situations.

Each week we will be sending home a note describing the skill and its steps. We hope that you review the weekly skill sheet with your child and help your child practice the skill at home. Please feel free to call me at _____ if you have any questions.

Sincerely,

_____

Skillstreaming in Early Childhood: New Strategies and Perspectives for Teaching Prosocial Skills
© 2003 by Ellen McGinnis and Arnold P. Goldstein. Champaign, IL: Research Press (800) 519–2707.

PARENT HOMEWORK NOTE 1

Student _____ Date _____

Dear Parent or Guardian:

This week we are working on the following skill:

_____

This is a very important skill for your child to learn. The steps of the skill are:

_____

_____

_____

_____

_____

Your child has completed a homework assignment on this skill. Please review this assignment with your child.

Please feel free to call if you have any questions.

Sincerely,

_____

PARENT HOMEWORK NOTE 2

Student _____ Date _____

Dear Parent or Guardian:

We are working on the following skill:

_____

This is a very important skill for your child to learn. The steps of the skill are:

_____

_____

_____

_____

_____

Your child has learned this skill well but will need continued practice. Please watch for the skill at home! If you see a situation when the skill could be used, please encourage your child to use this skill. Enclosed is a Parent Award to complete and return to school when you see your child use this skill.

Please feel free to call if you have any questions.

Sincerely,

_____

PARENT HOMEWORK NOTE 3

Student _____ Date _____

Dear Parent or Guardian:

Your child has been working on the following skill:

_____

This is a very important skill for your child to learn. The steps of the skill are:

_____

_____

_____

_____

_____

Your child has been asked to complete this skill at home. Please help your child to follow these skill steps.

Please sign and return this form to _____ with your comments (on the back) about quality of homework done and any questions/suggestions by _____.

Parent signature _____ Date _____

SKILLSTREAMING REQUEST TO PARENTS

Student _____ Date _____

Dear Parent or Guardian:

Your child is working on the following skill(s):

_____

_____

_____

_____

The steps to these skills are attached to this note. Please help your child practice at home by doing the following:

- Remind your child to use the skill when you see a time the skill could be helpful.
- Respond positively to your child's skill use (allow the skill use to be successful).
- Reward your child's use of the skill. (You may use a Parent Award and have your child return this to school.)
- Ask your child to teach you (or a brother or sister) the skill.
- Other _____

Please write any comments on the back of this form about how your child is learning and practicing this skill at home.

Sincerely,

_____